Thing

Written by **Paeony Lewis**

Illustrated by **Jonny Lambert**

OXFORD
UNIVERSITY PRESS

OXFORD
UNIVERSITY PRESS

Great Clarendon Street, Oxford, OX2 6DP, United Kingdom

Oxford University Press is a department of the University
of Oxford. It furthers the University's objective of excellence
in research, scholarship, and education by publishing
worldwide. Oxford is a registered trade mark of Oxford
University Press in the UK and in certain other countries

Text © Paeony Lewis 2017
Illustrations © Jonny Lambert 2017
Inside cover notes written by Liz Miles

The moral rights of the author have been asserted

First published 2017

British Library Cataloguing in Publication Data
Data available

ISBN: 978-0-19-841497-1

10 9 8 7 6 5 4 3 2 1

Paper used in the production of this book is a natural, recyclable product
made from wood grown in sustainable forests. The manufacturing process
conforms to the environmental regulations of the country of origin.

Printed in China by Golden Cup

Acknowledgements

Series Editor: Nikki Gamble

The meerkats are in the desert.
They see a spotty thing.

Fee runs to the spotty thing.

Look, Gus!

5

6

But Fee hooks the thing in the tree.

8

Fee jumps in her nest.

Fee has hurt her tail.

Sit down, Fee.

Soon the sun is back. The desert is hot again.